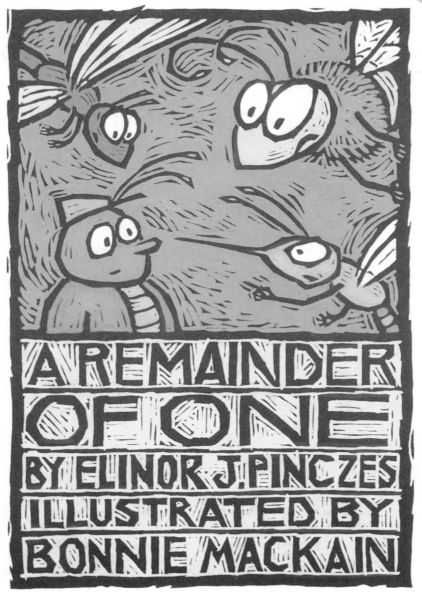

A REMAINDER OF ONE
BY ELINOR J. PINCZES
ILLUSTRATED BY BONNIE MACKAIN

Scholastic Inc.

New York Toronto London Auckland Sydney

To John, with love   —E.P.

For Bill   —B.S.M.

ISBN 0-590-76971-5

Text copyright © 1995 by Elinor J. Pinczes. Illustrations copyright © 1995 by Bonnie MacKain. All rights reserved. Published by Scholastic Inc., 555 Broadway, New York, NY 10012, by arrangement with Houghton Mifflin Company. SCHOLASTIC and associated logos are trademarks and/or registered trademarks of Scholastic Inc.

12 11 10 9 8 7 6 5 4 3 2   7 8 9/9 0 1 2/0

Printed in the U.S.A.   08

First Scholastic printing, October 1997

The story of Joe might just well explain
what happens to numbers when they must remain
after division, and they're left behind
as lonesome remainders. It seems so unkind!

Down by an orchard of young apple trees
the sunshine felt hot, about 90 degrees.

So insects all scurried for any cool shade;
from mushroom or leaf, they watched a parade.

The 25th squadron marched past the bug crowd,
bound and determined to make their queen proud.

The troop had divided by two for the show.
Each bug had a partner—except soldier Joe.

"Hup, two, three, four!
We're in the 25th Army Corps.

Queen's count! Two, three!
We are the marching infantry."

The queen wasn't pleased. "We're unhappy to find
that one soldier's left at the end of a line."

A honeybee hovered above lone Joe's head.
"The queen likes things tidy," the bee sternly said.

"I'm sorry, Private," said Joe's Sergeant Steven.
"You must stand aside, so the troop will be even."
The two lines of twelve then marched neatly away,
while bug-soldier Joe had no choice but to stay.

Lone soldier Joe learned it wasn't much fun
to find himself labeled "remainder of one"!
The brainy bug-soldier stayed up the whole night.
Perhaps one more line would make everything right?

All 25 soldiers marched past the bug crowd,
nervously hoping they'd make their queen proud.

The troop had divided by three for the show;
Each line seemed perfect. Then someone spied Joe.

"Hup, two, three, four!
We're in the 25th Army Corps.

Queen's count! Two, three!
We are the marching infantry."

The regal head shook. "It's disturbing to find
one oddball bug at the end of a line."

A slender mosquito loomed over Joe's head.
"Too bad you're a misfit," the pest sharply said.

"I'm sorry, Private," said Joe's Sergeant Steven.
"If you stand aside, then the troop will look even."
The three lines of eight all marched neatly away
while sad and disheartened, poor Joe had to stay.

The oddball bug Joe knew it wasn't much fun
to feel so left out—a remainder of one.
Again the lone soldier thought all through the night.
With one more bug line, it might work out right.

The 25th squadron marched past the bug crowd,
anxiously longing to make their queen proud.

The troop had divided by four for the show.
The lines all looked even, till they spotted Joe.

Her highness pointed. "We're angry to find
a tag-along bug at the end of one line."

A shy dragonfly fluttered over Joe's head.
"Now, don't get discouraged," the fly softly said.

"I'm sorry, Private," said Joe's Sergeant Steven.
"You must stand aside, then the troop will be even."
As four lines of six marched so neatly away,
sad Joe couldn't watch, for he had to stay.

Poor tag-along Joe didn't have any fun,
always left out—a remainder of one.
But hard-thinking Joe had the answer that night:
Another bug line *must* make it work right.

The 25th squadron marched past the proud queen.
The neatest, best troopers that she'd ever seen.

Five lines of soldiers with five in each row . . .
perfect at last—and that's *counting* Joe.

"Good show!" said her grace. "Your rows are divine.
We see no remainder to ruin your line."

The troop took great pride in their skill at dividing;
Joe was pleased he was there marching, not hiding.

The coolest bug-soldier beneath the hot sun?
Smart Joe, the former remainder of one!

DIVE IN

SENIOR AUTHOR

Leo Fay

AUTHORS

Barbara D. Stoodt
Dorothy Grant Hennings
Joan M. Baker
Myron L. Coulter

Bilingual Materials
  George A. González

The Riverside Publishing Company

Chicago ● Chamblee, Georgia ● Dallas, Texas ● Glendale, California ● Lawrenceville, New Jersey

Acknowledgments: We wish to thank the following publishers, authors, photographers, illustrators and agents for permission to use and adapt copyrighted materials.

"David's Windows" adapted by Alice Low from her book DAVID'S WINDOWS. Copyright ©1974 by Alice Low. Used by permission of the author.
"Down in a Haystack" based on DEEP IN A HAYSTACK written by Michael Sage. Copyright ©1966 by Michael Sage. Adapted by permission of Viking Penguin Inc.
"Fly Pretty Bird" by Gladys Weeks was first published in KIKIRIKI: STORIES AND POEMS IN ENGLISH AND SPANISH FOR CHILDREN. (Houston: University of Houston Arte Publico Press, 1981.)
"One More Thing, Dad" adapted from ONE MORE THING, DAD, text ©1980 by Susan L. Thompson. Reprinted with the permission of Albert Whitman & Company.
"The Rainbow" text and illustrations adapted from "The Rainbow" in MOKE AND POKI IN THE RAIN FOREST by Mamoru Funai. An I CAN READ book. Copyright ©1972 by Mamoru Funai. Reprinted by permission of Harper & Row, Publishers.
"A Rainbow for Me" from A RAINBOW OF MY OWN by Don Freeman. Copyright ©1966 by Don Freeman. Adapted by permission of Viking Penguin Inc. All rights reserved. First published in Great Britain 1967 by World's Work Ltd.
"Raindrops" from OUT IN THE DARK AND DAYLIGHT by Aileen Fisher. Copyright ©1966 by Aileen Fisher. Reprinted by permission of Harper & Row, Publishers, Inc.
"Sun After Rain" from SMALL WONDERS by Norma Farber. Text Copyright ©1964, 1968, 1979 by Norma Farber. Reprinted by permission of The Putnam Publishing Group.
"A Year Later" from HELLO AND GOOD-BY by Mary Ann Hoberman. Copyright ©1959 by Mary Ann Hoberman. Reprinted by permission of Russell & Volkening, Inc. as agents for the author.

ILLUSTRATIONS: YVETTE BANEK 149–158, 166–173 KRIS BOYD 126–130 JAN BRETT 117–125 LISA CAMPBELL ERNST 50–58 PAT CUMMINGS 34–41 JIM DEIGAN 49, 131 ANDREA EBERBACH 60–69 MAMORU FUNAI 99–108 MICHELE GUIRE VAKA 42–48 LUCINDA McQUEEN 141–148 SAL MURDOCCA 76–82 ANN NEWMAN 59, 83–88, 165 MICHELE NOISET 28–33, 109 JAN PYK 70–74, 110–116 DOROTHEA SIERRA 5, 89 GLORIA SINGER 159–164 JERRY SMATH 8–15, 132, 140 MARTI SHOET 16, 90–98 FREYA TANZ 18–26

PHOTOGRAPHY: MARIAN BERNSTEIN 27–33 NASA 164 THE GRANGER COLLECTION 162 WALT DISNEY PRODUCTIONS 163

COVER ART: Tom Powers / Mulvey Associates

CONTENTS

How to Learn New Words

1. Look at the letters in the word.

2. Think of the sound clues.

3. Use the sentence clues.

4. Read the word.

How to Read for Meaning

1. Set a purpose.

2. Read the story.

3. Answer the question.

6

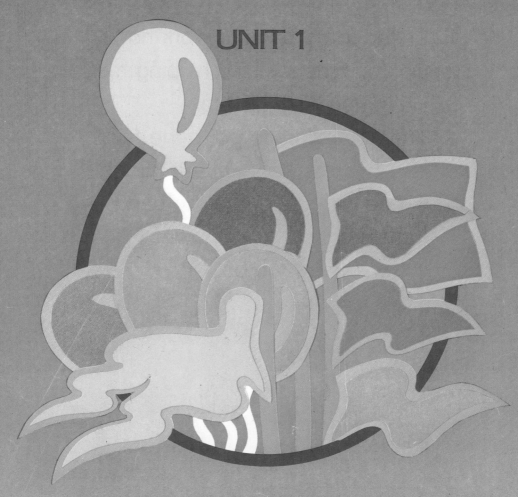

UNIT 1

HURRAH!

LEARN NEW WORDS

1. I need to go **back** to work now.
2. Do you girls **feel** like helping me?
3. He jumped on the **box**.
4. The boys want to go to the **fair**.
5. The **band** will play at the fair.
6. **Come** with us to see the band.
7. I am **happy** to work now.
8. We will **paint** the box.

8

NED and the GRAND STREET FAIR

by CASSANDRA COOK

It was going to be a big day.
It was the day of the Grand Street Fair.
Ned looked at the people helping.
The people looked happy.

"I want to help with the fair, too,"
said Ned.
"But what can I do?
I have to find what I can do best."

9

Ned went to see what Marty was doing.
"Do you need help?" he said.

"We do need help," Marty said.
"Do you feel like playing in the band?"

"I like bands.
And I feel like playing," Ned said.
"I am happy to help you."

10

Ned jumped up on a box.
He played with the band a little.
"This is fun," he said.
"But this is not for me.
I have to find what I do best.
I do want to help with the fair."

Then Mike said, "Do you want
to help me?"
Ned was happy.
He wanted to help Mike.

11

"Do magic as I do," said Mike.
"See what is in this hat."

The hat had lots of handkerchiefs in it.
"How did all this get in the hat?"
said Ned.

"That hat is not as little
as it looks," Mike said.

"You do the best magic!"
Ned said.
"I like what you do.
But I have to find out what I do best."

12

Then Ned did not feel happy.
He did not want to go back to the band.
He did not want to do magic.
"What can I do to help?" he said.
"What can I do best?"

"I have it!" he said.
"I can paint posters.
I can tell people what there is to see
at the fair."

Ned jumped back up on a box.
He got out all the paints he had.

13

Then Ned looked at all the people.

He painted a poster of the band.
He painted a poster of Mike
and the hat.
He painted a poster
of the people working.
Then Marty helped Ned make
a big poster.
It said, "Come to
the Grand Street Fair."

Mike and Marty did like the posters.
"Posters are what this fair needs!"
Marty said.
"You make the best posters!"

Mike helped Ned find places
for the posters.
All the people did like the posters.

Ned was happy.
"I did find out what I do best!"

Ned went back up on the box.
"Come on in!" he yelled.
All the people looked at Ned.
"Come have fun at the fair!"

COME TO THE
GRAND STREET
FAIR

SEE MAGIC

HAVE FUN at the FAIR

15

A Year Later

by MARY ANN HOBERMAN

Last summer I couldn't swim at all;
I couldn't even float!
I had to use a rubber tube
Or hang on to a boat;
I had to sit on shore
While everybody swam.
But now it's this summer
And I can!

16

LEARN NEW WORDS

1. Water makes a **fire** go out.
2. The girls and boys are **nice** to me.
3. He can find rocks in the **caves**.
4. He **lost** a ball in the yard.
5. There is **gold** in that sack.
6. The bird **hurt** a wing.
7. My **friends** will take me home.
8. The magician can **change** the rabbit to a pig.

17

Prince William and Duncan Dragon

by LOIS ALLEN

Prince William had no friends.
He yelled all the time.
Boys and girls did not want
to play with Prince William.

"I will find a dragon," said William.
"The dragon will be my friend."

18

Prince William went to the magician.
"Magician, get me a dragon!" he yelled.

"You can't have a dragon as a friend,"
said the magician.
"A dragon is big and has fire.
Fire can hurt you."

"Change the dragon!" yelled the Prince.

"I do not like yelling,"
said the magician.
"But I will do what you want."

The magician said, "Abracadabra!"
There was Duncan Dragon!
He was little and did not make fire.

"Play with me!" yelled Prince William.

But Duncan Dragon did not want to play.
He did not look at all happy.
"Why am I little?" said Duncan.
"Where is my fire?"

"Fire hurts!" yelled Prince William.

"You are not nice," said Duncan.
"You yell all the time.
You made the magician change me.
Now I do not feel like me.
Tell the magician to change me back.
I want to be a big dragon with fire.
I will not hurt you."

"Will you be my friend then?"
said Prince William.

21

"Be nice and do not yell," said Duncan.
"Then I will be a friend.
We will play all day.
You will have lots of friends.
But you will have to change me back!"

"Change back the dragon," said
Prince William to the magician.
Prince William did not yell this time.

"Abracadabra!" said the magician.

22

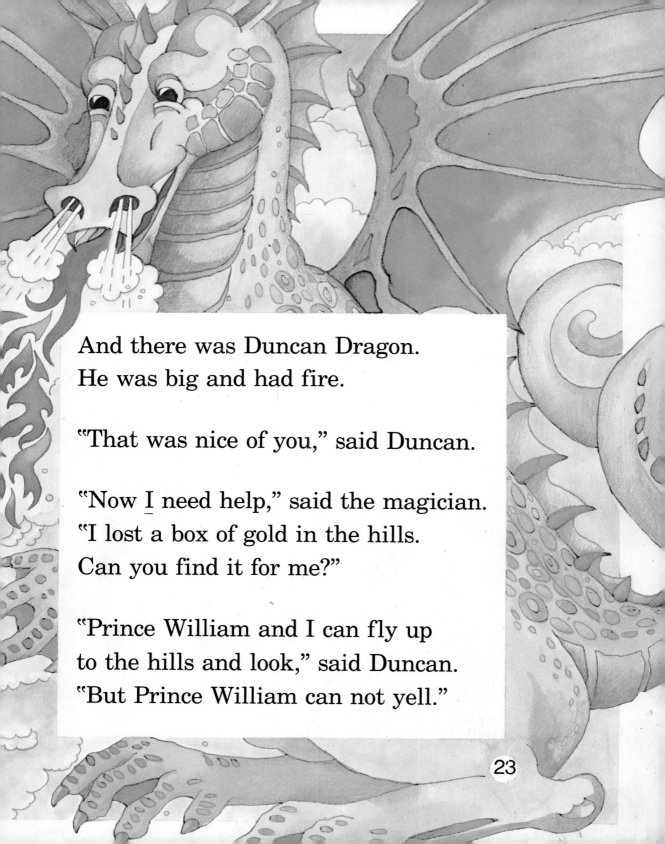

And there was Duncan Dragon.
He was big and had fire.

"That was nice of you," said Duncan.

"Now I need help," said the magician.
"I lost a box of gold in the hills.
Can you find it for me?"

"Prince William and I can fly up
to the hills and look," said Duncan.
"But Prince William can not yell."

Prince William looked happy.
"I want to fly all day!" he yelled.

"No yelling," said the dragon.

Prince William jumped on the dragon.
Up the dragon went.
He went as high as the hills.

"There are caves in the hills,"
said Duncan Dragon.
"I will land there."

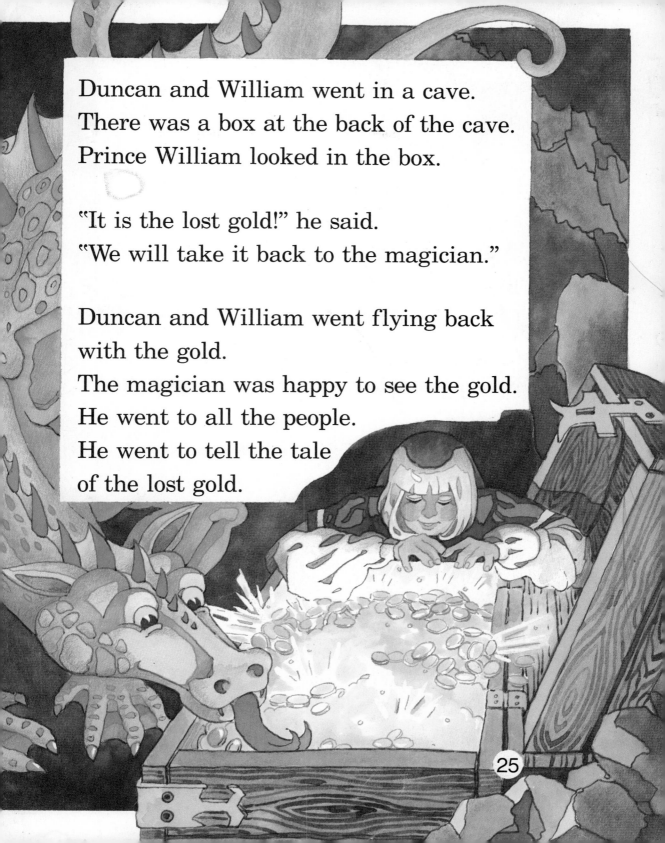

Duncan and William went in a cave.
There was a box at the back of the cave.
Prince William looked in the box.

"It is the lost gold!" he said.
"We will take it back to the magician."

Duncan and William went flying back
with the gold.
The magician was happy to see the gold.
He went to all the people.
He went to tell the tale
of the lost gold.

25

The boys and girls all wanted to see Prince William.

Prince William looked at the boys and girls.
"I have changed," he said.
"I do not yell now.
I helped the magician.
And I have Duncan as a friend.
Now I want to be friends with you, too!"

"This is the best day," said Duncan to Prince William.
"You will have friends for all time!"

26

LEARN NEW WORDS

1. That boy can **fix** a fence.
2. The girls did the job **well**.
3. What **things** can you do?
4. You can see the people **dance**.
5. He can play a nice **song**.
6. He likes to water the **plants**.
7. The **puppy** has a new home.
8. **Think** of all there is to do!

You Can Do It!

by CYNTHIA LEWIN

What things do you like to do?
Think of what is fun.

Now, come look at all you can do.

28

The boys and girls like to jump.
You can jump, too.
Jump in and out.
Jump up and back.
Jump high, high up!

This band is playing a song.
Do you think you can make up a song?
Make up a fast, happy song.

People like to dance to a song.
I like to dance.
Do you think I dance well?

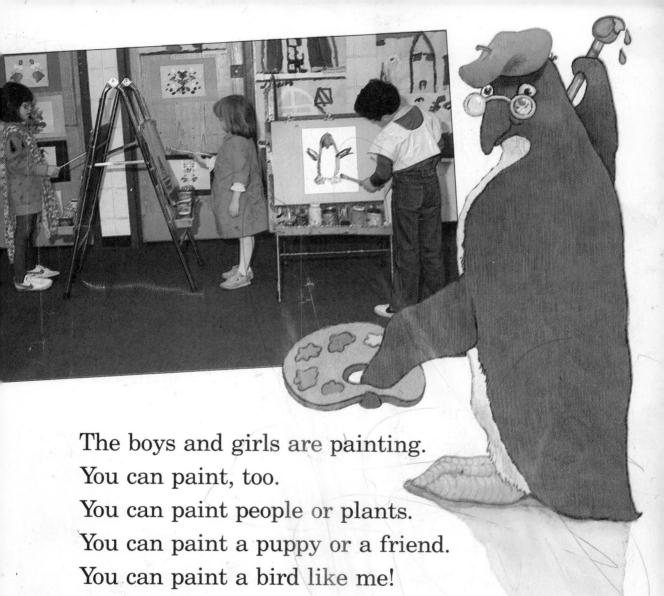

The boys and girls are painting.
You can paint, too.
You can paint people or plants.
You can paint a puppy or a friend.
You can paint a bird like me!

Now look at me.
I will paint you.
I can do it, too!

31

Look in this yard.
See how all the friends work.
That is how to do things fast.
Find friends to work with.

There are a lot of things to do.
Work on the plants.
Help fix the fence.
Get water for the puppy.

You can work like this, too.
You can work well with friends.

32

Did you see all the things you can do?
You can think of new things, too.
You can find things to fix.
You can make a costume.
You can help a pet.

What do you like to do?
Think of what is best for you.

LEARN NEW WORDS

1. Do not run or you will **fall**.
2. I paint with this **hand**.
3. He **reads** lots of things
   on animals.
4. The girl hurt **her** hand.
5. You can **hold** my new puppy.
6. The girls are my **sisters**.
7. The girl dances and **turns** fast.
8. **She** is going to play
   with the paints.

34

I Am Me!

by CHARLOTTE MARQUARDT

Nikki and Jill are sisters.
Jill is big.
Nikki is little.

Nikki and Jill like to do a lot
of things.
The sisters work and play at home.
Nikki and Jill are sisters
and friends, too.

Nikki has a lot of fun.
She likes to play with her puppy.
She likes to run fast down a hill.
She likes to paint.

Jill likes to do lots of things, too.
She reads a lot.
She dances and turns fast.
Jill has a big collection of animals.

36

Nikki wants to do the things
her big sister can do.

"I want to dance and turn like you,"
said Nikki.
"But I do not want to fall down."

"Hold my hand," said Jill.

Jill helped Nikki dance and turn.
Nikki did not fall.

37

Nikki said, "Can I play
with the animal collection?
I want to hold the rabbit, the cat,
and the bird in my hands.
The animals will not fall."

"You can play with my collection,"
Jill said.

Nikki had fun with the animals.
She turned the animals back to back
on the bed.

Nikki has a friend, Dori.
Dori likes to visit Nikki.
Nikki likes Dori a lot.
But Nikki will not play with Dori
all the time.

"Do you want to run now?" said Dori.
"Or can we play with the puppy?"

"I do not want to run now," said Nikki.
"I do not want to play at all.
I want to dance and turn with Jill.
She holds my hand and helps me."

"You are not fun to be with,"
said Dori.
"You do not do what you like.
You want to do what Jill likes to do."

Nikki was quiet.
She was thinking.

"You play with all of her animals,"
said Dori.
"You want to dance and turn with her.
You read what she reads."

40

"I see that now," said Nikki.
"I like Jill a lot.
I like the things Jill can do.
But I like to run fast, too.
I like my puppy.
And I like to play with you, Dori.
I can be a sister for Jill.
I can be a friend for Jill and for you.
And I can be <u>me</u>, too!"

41

No Place Like Home

by ALICE LOW

"I am going to make a new home,"
Pinky Pig said to Duffy Pig.

Duffy said, "I am going to make
a new home, too."

"I will make the best home,"
Pinky said.
"No water will get in my home."

Duffy said, "Well, no water
will get in my home."

"I will use rocks," Pinky said.

"You can't make a home with rocks,"
Duffy said.

"I can and I will," Pinky said.

Duffy said, "I will use a box."

"You can't use a box," Pinky said.

"I can and I will," Duffy said.

43

Pinky and Duffy worked and worked.
"This is a big job," said the pigs.

Then Pinky said, "I will place
plants on top."

"You can't make a home with plants
on top," Duffy said.

Pinky said, "I can and I will."

Duffy said, "Then I will place a fence on top."

"You can't make a home with a fence on top," Pinky said.

Duffy said, "I can and I will."

The pigs worked and worked. Then Duffy looked up.

45

"You will get water in that rock home,"
Duffy said to Pinky.

Pinky said, "I am fixing it.
Look there!
Water will get in that box home."

Duffy said, "I will fix that.
You will see how I fix it.
No water will get in."

46

Pinky said, "See the water come down?
I will go in my nice new home."

Duffy said, "I will go in <u>my</u> home, too."

There was a lot of water.
But the water did not get in the homes.

47

Then Pinky said, "I feel at home
in my new home.
It is made of rocks."

"I feel at home in <u>my</u> new home.
I made it with this box and that box,"
Duffy said.

Then happy Pinky and Duffy
made up a song.
"The homes have made us happy,
as happy as can be.
<u>That</u> home is nice for you,
and <u>this</u> home is nice for me."

48

Small Things

LEARN NEW WORDS

1. The can is **filled** to the top with paint.
2. That box has a **flat** top.
3. Her visits **mean** a lot to us.
4. She **asked** Meg for a hat.
5. I will help **move** the big box.
6. **Thank** you for all the help.
7. **Your** help made us happy.
8. She wants a **drink** of water.
9. She **smiled** at Meg.

50

Little Things Mean a Lot

by ROSS ELIOT

"This place needs to be painted,"
Grandma said.
"I am going to paint it.
I can use your help, Meg."

"How can I help you, Grandma?"
asked Meg.

"You can do lots of little things,"
said Grandma.
"Little things can be a big help.
Little things mean a lot."

51

Then Grandma went to work.
She had to move all the furniture.
But she did not want to move
the box filled with plants.

"Do you want me to move this box
for you?" Meg asked.

"No, Meg," Grandma said.
"But you can help me place
newspapers on things."

"Can I get the cans of paint
for you?" Meg asked.

"No, thank you," Grandma smiled.
"The cans are filled with paint.
They are too big.
But you <u>can</u> go get the big paintbrushes."

53

Grandma painted with a flat paintbrush.
The flat paintbrush helped make
the work go fast.

"Painting looks like fun," said Meg.
"Can I do it, Grandma?"

54

"No, your hand is too little to use
this big paintbrush.
But you can help me take
this thing down," said Grandma.

55

Meg was a big help to Grandma.
She did like to help.

Then Meg made a hat
out of newspaper.

"This is your paint hat," Meg said.
"The paint will get on the hat and
not on you!"

Grandma smiled at Meg.
"A paint hat is a little thing.
But it will be a big help!
Thank you, Meg," she said.

"Will you get me a little water
now, Meg?
I need it for the paint,"
Grandma said.

Meg went to get the water
for the paint.
She got a drink of water, too.
Then she got a drink of water
for Grandma.

"Thank you," Grandma smiled.
"The paint needed water, and I did, too!
A little drink of water can mean
a lot."

57

"Now I have to paint in back
of the plant box.
But my hand is too big to do that.
What am I going to do?" Grandma asked.

"Can you find a little, flat paintbrush
for me, Grandma?" Meg asked.

Grandma said, "I think I can."

"I can fit <u>my</u> hand in back
of the plant box," Meg said.
"Little things <u>do</u> mean a lot!"

58

Raindrops

by AILEEN FISHER

How brave a ladybug must be!
Each drop of rain is big as she.

Can you imagine what you'd do
if raindrops fell as big as you?

LEARN NEW WORDS

1. We **cleaned** the yard.
2. He wants to play with **his** pet.
3. There is a **gift** for you in that box!
4. That **house** is on a big hill.
5. The bird worked on a new **nest**.
6. He made a **paper** animal.
7. The girl **sang** a happy song.
8. Is the big gift **from** you?
9. A puppy is a **small** animal.

A Gift from Paco

by GARY BARGAR

"Paco, where is your smile?" asked Mom.
"This is a happy day for all of us.
Dad has a birthday!"

"I am not happy," said Paco.
"I do not have a nice big gift
for Dad."

61

"A small gift is nice," said Mom.
"Why not make a small gift?
Dad will like that."

"What can I make?" asked Paco.

"That is up to you," said Mom.
"I have to go in the house now.
You will think of a nice gift."

Paco went in the yard.

He looked at all the things there.

There was his box of rocks.

"But rocks are not a gift Dad will like,"
he said.

Then there was his box of little
play people.

"My play people are not the best gift
for Dad," he said.

Paco did not smile at all.

63

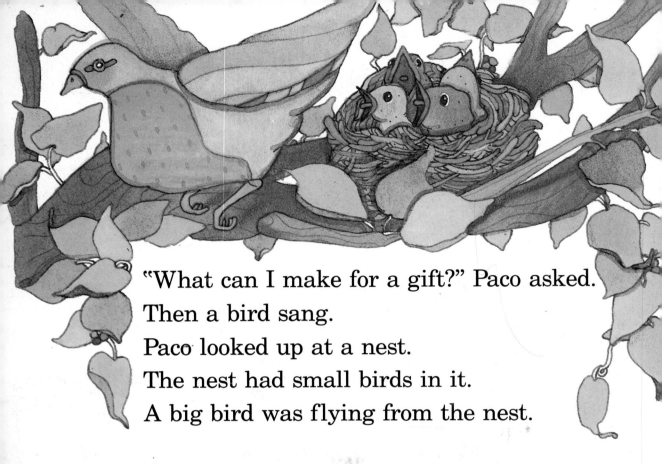

"What can I make for a gift?" Paco asked.
Then a bird sang.
Paco looked up at a nest.
The nest had small birds in it.
A big bird was flying from the nest.

"Dad likes to look at birds," said Paco.
"That is what I will make for Dad.
I will make a paper bird.
It will be like the bird on top
of my box."

Paco went in the house.

Paco cleaned his work place.
He cleaned his paintbrushes.
Then he got out his paper
and his water paints.
He had to work fast.

"This new bird will look like the bird
I made," Paco said.
"It will have a beak and wings, too."

65

Mom looked in and said, "Paco,
it is time to clean up.
All the people have come to the house.
It is time for Dad to come home."

"Now there is no time to make my gift,"
Paco said.

He looked at his work.
There was no time to make the new bird.
Paco looked at the bird on his box.
That bird looked nice.

"I think I have a gift, Mom!" Paco said.

66

Paco went to hide
with all the people.

Then Dad got home.
All the people jumped up.
Then they all sang,
"Happy Birthday."

"You mean all this is for me?"
Dad asked.
"What a nice surprise!"

Then Paco said, "Dad, this paper bird
is a gift from me.
I made it for you!
Do you like small gifts like this?"

"This is a nice gift!" Dad said.
"And <u>you</u> made this gift.
That means a lot to me.
No one fixes up a gift like you do."

Paco smiled and smiled.
Now it was a happy day for Paco, too.

LEARN NEW WORDS

1. **Cut** the paper at the top.
2. **Put** the bird in the nest.
3. We can paint the house **red**.
4. I **sleep** in a bed.
5. **Fold** your paper flat like this.
6. I need to use **half** of this paper.
7. **Next**, fold the red paper in half.
8. Hold the bird **under** the wings.
9. The bird has **green** wings.

FUN
with
PAPER

by DENNIS SILLARI

You can make a paper bird
like Paco did.
It is fun to make.
You can make yours
red and green, too!

Look at the things you will need.
Put the things where you work.

Now look at 1.

1. Take your paper and
   fold it in half.
   Then cut it with your
    .

2. Next, take half the paper.
   Make a big oval on it.

3. Now cut the oval out.

71

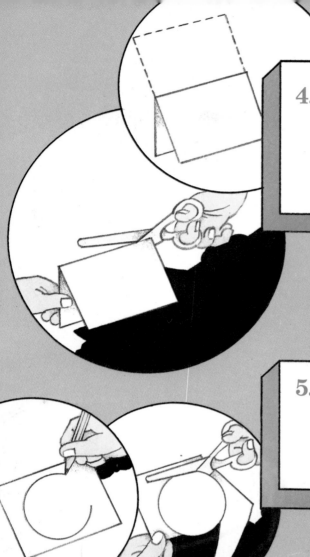

4. Next, take the half
   you did not use.
   Fold it in half
   and cut it.

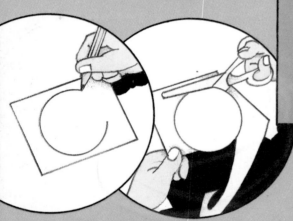

5. Take a half and make
   a circle on it.
   Then cut the circle out.

6. Paste the circle
   on the oval like this.

72

7. There is a half
   you have not cut.
   Take it and cut it
   like this.
   Now you have the wings.

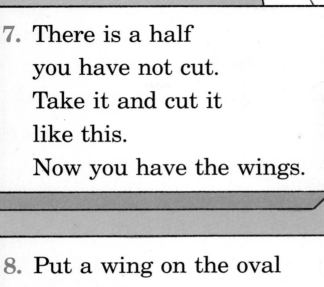

8. Put a wing on the oval
   like this.
   Then turn the oval.
   Put a wing there, too!

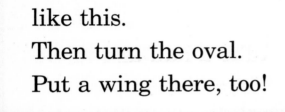

9. Now fold the wings down.

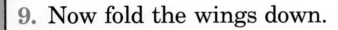

10. Make a beak.
    Paste it on the circle.

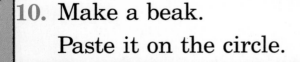

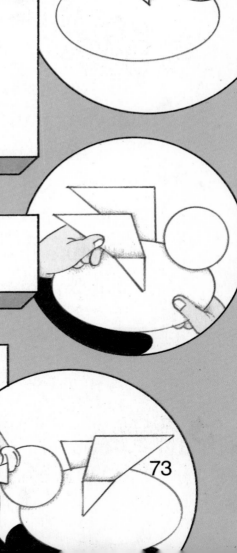

Now paint your bird red and green.
Make the beak red and the wings green.
Paint under the wings, too!

Where do birds sleep?
Birds sleep in nests.
Make a nest to put under the bird.
Then the bird can sleep in it.

Can you make the bird fly?
Put your hand under the bird.
Then move your hand up and down.

You can play with the bird
and make it fly.
It can be your friend.

74

1. That big thing is made from **oak**.
2. Birds fly up **when** people come next to the nest.
3. My friends will visit for a **long** time.
4. The girls had to **push** the big box.
5. The rabbit hides **behind** the big rock.
6. The boy **watched** his pets play.
7. Red **flowers** are nice.
8. The birds made nests in the oak **trees**.
9. When she asked, we sang **another** song.

BESS HELPS OUT

by JUDY ROSENBAUM

Kim was flying under the oak trees.
She was holding her new red balloon.
Bess watched Kim fly up, down,
and backward.

"What a nice balloon you have,"
said Bess to her friend.
Bess went to hold the balloon.

"Watch where you put your quills!"
yelled Kim.
But Bess did not watch out.

"My balloon!" said Kim.

But it was not a balloon now.
It was a long, flat, red thing.

"I did not mean to hurt your balloon,"
said Bess.
"I will fix it for you."

The bird said, "A balloon can't be fixed.
You are my friend, Bess.
But you can't play with balloons.
Your quills are too long."

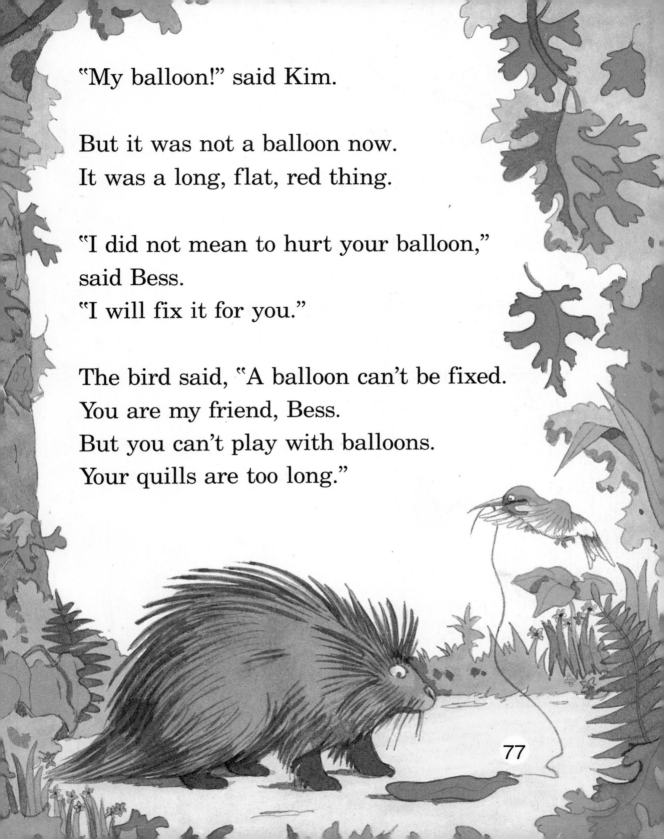

The next day, Bess went to see Kim.
The bird was fixing her nest.

"Can I help?" asked Bess.

Kim said, "You can look
for green plants and flowers.
That is how I fix my nest."

Bess was happy to help.
She sang as she looked
behind rocks and oak trees.
She got a lot of flowers
and green plants for the nest.

Bess went back to the nest.

"Watch out for my nest!"
yelled Kim.

Bess did not mean to push
the nest down.
But she did.
Then she landed on it.

Kim said, "Bess, I like you.
But you are no help when
I am fixing my nest."
Kim went to find flowers
for another nest.

Bess was not happy at all.
"I am not the best friend
for a little bird," she said.
"Thanks to me, Kim
has no balloon and no nest.
She needs another friend."

Then Kim yelled, "Help! Help!"

Bess went to see what Kim needed.

Bess went to a big oak tree.
She looked for the bird there.

Kim said, "Bess!
Look behind you.
I am behind this big rock.
I have pushed and pushed at it.
But I am too small.
I can't get out."

Bess said, "I can push
the rock.
Get out when I push on it."

Bess pushed the rock.
Down it went.
Out went Kim.

"Thank you, Bess!" said Kim.
"You are my best friend.
You are there when I need you."

Now Bess was happy.
"That is what friends are for," she said.

HUMMINGBIRDS

by DUNCAN SEARL

This is a bird zoo.
It has a place for hummingbirds.
Can you see the hummingbirds?
Three of the hummingbirds are green.
Three of the birds are red.

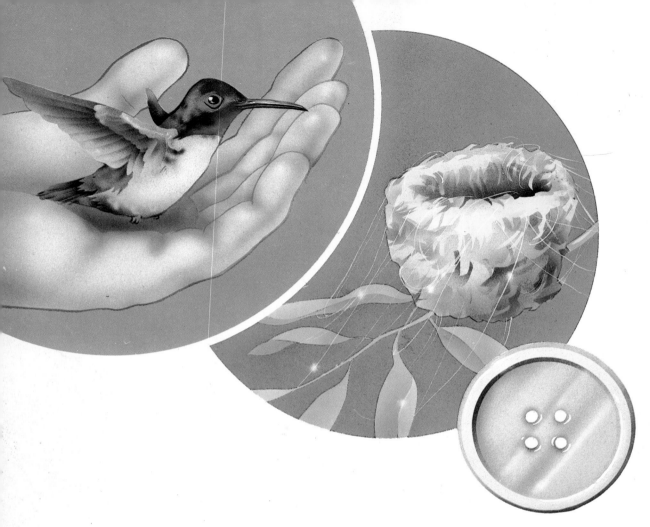

A hummingbird is a small, small bird.
It can fit in your hand!

A hummingbird nest is little, too.
The hummingbird nest is as little
as the button next to it!

Hummingbirds have long, long beaks.
Long beaks help the birds drink.
Hummingbirds have to drink
50 or 60 times a day!

This bird is drinking now.
It has put its beak in a flower.
This is how it drinks from the flower.

Hummingbirds fly fast.
Hummingbird wings move too fast
for us to see.

Hummingbird wings can turn, too.
When the wings turn down,
the hummingbird will fly down.
When the wings turn up,
the bird will fly up.
The wings can turn to the back, too.
Then the bird will fly backward!

Hummingbirds can not run.
But the birds can fly in place.

Look at this hummingbird make a nest.
The <u>wings</u> move up and down fast.
But the <u>hummingbird</u> will not move
up or down.

You can look for hummingbirds.
The birds fly to a lot of places.

You can have a hummingbird visit you.
This is what you have to do.
Plant red flowers in your yard.
Hummingbirds like red best.
You can put red things
in your yard, too.

Will you see a hummingbird?
Watch and see.

UNIT 3

Rainbows

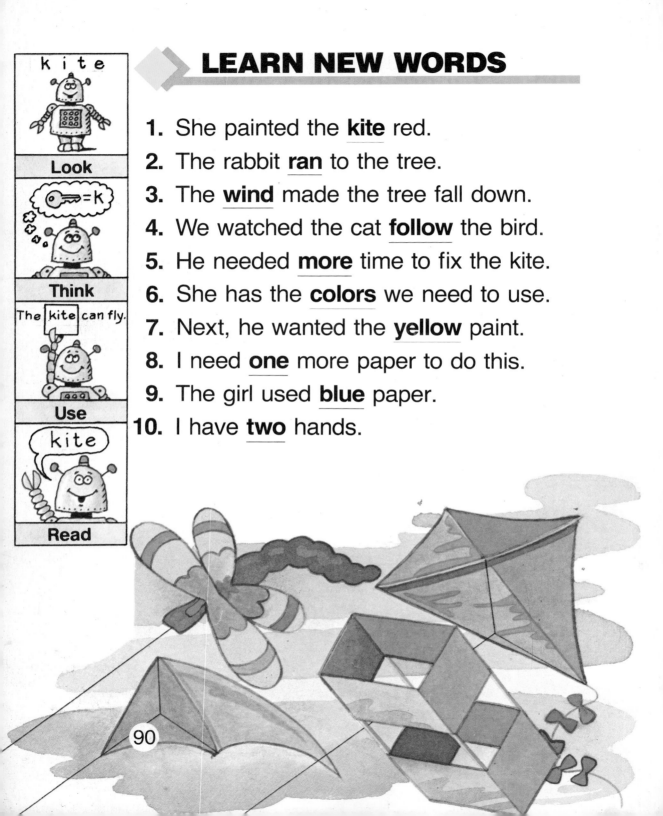

LEARN NEW WORDS

k i t e
Look

Think

The kite can fly.

Use

kite

Read

1. She painted the **kite** red.
2. The rabbit **ran** to the tree.
3. The **wind** made the tree fall down.
4. We watched the cat **follow** the bird.
5. He needed **more** time to fix the kite.
6. She has the **colors** we need to use.
7. Next, he wanted the **yellow** paint.
8. I need **one** more paper to do this.
9. The girl used **blue** paper.
10. I have **two** hands.

90

The Kite Contest

by ELIZABETH EMERY

Come to Kite Contest Day
Best Kites Win!

"The Kite Contest is in two days, Teri.
We need a kite!" Amy said to her sister.

"Why one kite?" Teri asked.
"We have a lot of friends with kites.
We can all fly kites at one time.
Then we will win."

Amy ran to find her friends.
Teri ran to find her friends.

91

All the boys and girls had blue
or yellow kites.
Amy and Teri had yellow kites.
Lee had a yellow kite, too.
Kate, Rob, and Jack had blue kites.

"I think we need more colors!" said Amy.
"We can't win with two colors."

"I have the paints we need at home,"
said Teri.
"We can change the colors on the kites.
Follow me."

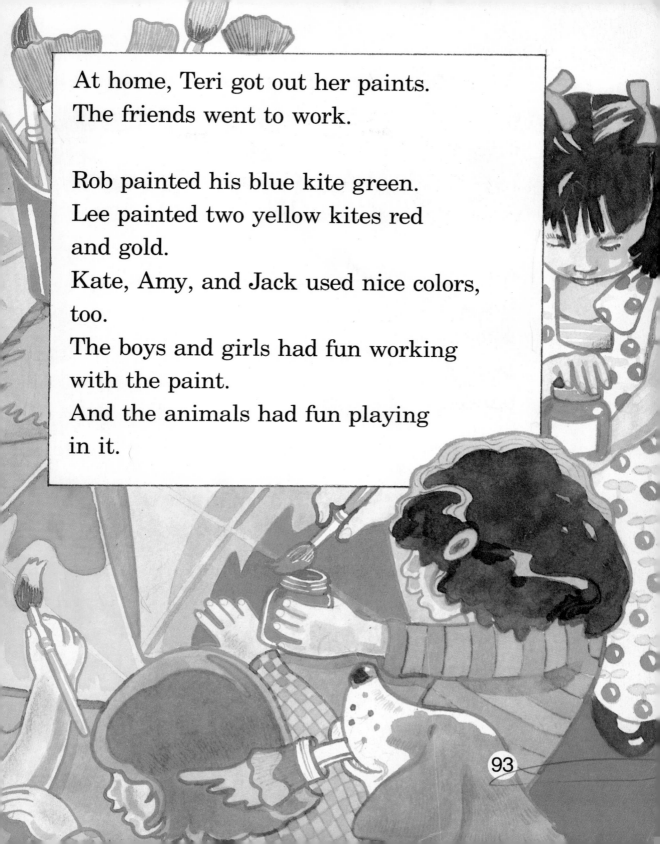

At home, Teri got out her paints.
The friends went to work.

Rob painted his blue kite green.
Lee painted two yellow kites red
and gold.
Kate, Amy, and Jack used nice colors,
too.
The boys and girls had fun working
with the paint.
And the animals had fun playing
in it.

93

The next day, the friends ran to fly
the kites.
There was a big wind.
In no time at all, the kites
danced in the wind.

"We have all the colors now," said Amy.
"But the kites look too small
up there.
Small kites disappear up there."

Teri said, "We can put long
paper streamers on the kites.
That will help the kites look big."

94

The boys and girls followed Teri
back home.
Teri got out more paper and paint.
The friends worked fast to make
the streamers.

"Do you think the kites will fly
with the streamers on?" asked Amy.

But there was no time to find out.
The next day was Kite Contest Day.

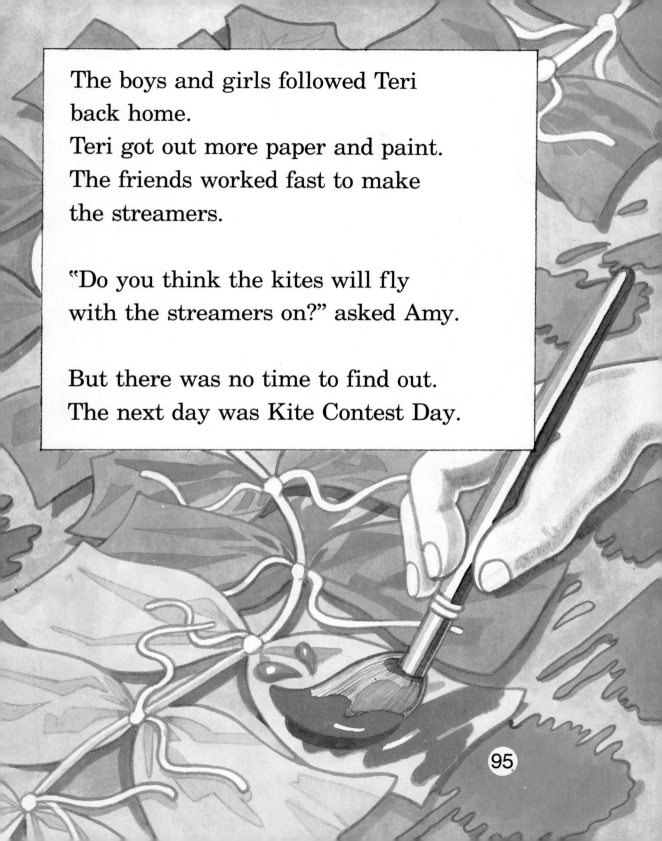

A lot of people had come to see
the kites fly on Kite Contest Day.
But the boys and girls
did not look happy.
There was no wind.

"We need wind to fly the kites
and the streamers," said Amy.
"What will we do?"

96

Then a big wind filled the place.

"Come on!" yelled Teri.
"This is the wind we need."

Up went a kite.
One more kite followed it.
Then the next and the next went up.

"Look up there!" yelled a girl.
"Look at all the colors.
It is a rainbow of kites!"

97

All the people looked up.
"The rainbow of kites wins,"
said the people.

"We have the best kites!"
yelled the friends.
"We win the Kite Contest!"

98

LEARN NEW WORDS

1. His friend **came** with us to the play.
2. The boy **sat** on the rock.
3. Have you **seen** all the colors?
4. It feels nice when the **sun** comes out!
5. The house looked **better** when it was painted.
6. That big hat looks **funny** on you.
7. He has **never** played ball that well!
8. He watched the **rain** fall.
9. **They** played in the sun.
10. I like the color **purple** best of all.

THE RAINBOW

adapted from a story
by MAMORU FUNAI

Moke sat on a rock.
He looked out at the rain valley.
He sat there for a long time.

Then he made up this song:

Rainbow, rainbow that I see,
Colors that look nice to me.
There is red, and there is blue,
Yellow, green, and purple, too.

"What are you doing?" said Poki.

"I am watching for the rainbow,"
said Moke.

"A rainbow!" said Poki.
"What a funny thing to do."

101

Nene-goose, Mouse, Dog, and Green Frog
came from the forest.

"What are you doing?" asked Mouse.

"I am watching for the rainbow,"
said Moke.

"That is a funny thing to do,"
said Nene-goose.
"There are better things to do."

102

Dog and Green Frog said,
"A rainbow! Ha, ha, ha, ha!
That is funny!"

"Come on," said Poki.
"Come on and play."

Poki, Nene-goose, Mouse, Dog, and
Green Frog went to the rain forest.

But then the sun disappeared.
The rain came down.
They all ran under a plant.

103

"Well, what can we do now?"
said Nene-goose.

"There are lots of things we can do,"
said Poki.

"Can you think of <u>one</u>?" asked Mouse.

"No, not now," said Dog.

"Well, neither can I,"
said Green Frog.

They sat and watched the rain fall.

"Why did Moke want to see
a rainbow?" said Nene-goose.

"I think he has never seen
a rainbow," said Poki.

"Have you seen a rainbow?"
asked Mouse.

"I do not think I have,"
said Nene-goose.

"Come to think of it, I have never
seen a rainbow," said Poki.

"Neither have we,"
said Dog and Green Frog.

"Well, we can watch
for Moke's rainbow," said Poki.

Moke sat on the rock
under a big plant.

"Did the rainbow come?"
said Poki.

"No," said Moke.

"Can we watch with you?" said Poki.

"You can," said Moke.

106

Poki, Nene-goose, Mouse, Dog, and
Green Frog sat under Moke's big plant.
They looked out at the rain valley.

Then the sun came out.
A nice, big rainbow came.
Then another and another.
The rain valley was filled
with rainbows.

"Look at the red and the purple!"
they said.

It made Moke and his friends happy.
Then they clapped hands and sang
this song:

> Rainbows, rainbows come to you.
> Yellow, green, and purple, too.
> When it rains and we can't play,
> We watch rainbows all the day.

Sun After Rain

by NORMA FARBER

Rain, rain,
went away.
Sun came out
with pipe of clay,
blew a bubble
whole-world-wide,
stuck a rainbow
on one side.

LEARN NEW WORDS

1. She has on a red **dress**.
2. She **mixed** the paints.
3. What is the **name** of that color?
4. There is paint in the **pail**.
5. The **leaves** are green.
6. We can mix **many** new colors.
7. Can you find **something** new there?
8. We will make **other** colors.
9. This is the **way** to do better work.
10. How can you make the color **orange**?

ALL THAT COLOR!

by DAN ROSEN

Charlie likes colors.
Charlie will find out
why three colors are important.
He will find a way to make
other colors.

Look at Charlie push the pail.
What color is in the pail?
What color is the fox?
What other red things do you see?
Red is one important color.

What is Charlie up to now?
Charlie is finding another
important color.
The name of this color is yellow.
Many things are yellow.
The sun is yellow.
Lemons are yellow, too.

Charlie, look at the dress.
What color is the dress?

112

Now Charlie wants to see what is
in this pail.
Look out, Charlie!
Now the blue paint is on Charlie.

The color blue is important, too.
Look at the blue whale.

Now look at your friends.
Do you see a blue dress or button?
Name something that is blue.

Look at the next two pails.
One pail has blue paint in it.
The other pail has yellow in it.

Blue and yellow can be mixed.
That is the way to make the color green.
Green is the color of many leaves.

Charlie likes playing in the leaves.

Can you see something small and green
playing in the leaves?

Charlie looks in two more pails.
Red and yellow can be mixed, too.
That is the way to make
the color orange.

Orange is the color of oranges!
They make a nice drink.

Now Charlie is behind something.
Where are you hiding, Charlie?

115

Charlie sees two more pails of paint!
They are red and blue.
Red and blue can be mixed.
That is the way to make
the color purple.
Purple plums come from trees.

Look out, Charlie!
Can you name the other thing
that is purple?

Now Charlie sees why red, yellow,
and blue are important colors.
The colors can be mixed to make
many new ones.

LEARN NEW WORDS

1. They sat down next to the **creek**.
2. The birds sat on the **grass**.
3. The rabbit has a **tail**.
4. The **deer** was drinking water.
5. She will look in the **open** box to see what is in it.
6. The girl **saw** a blue bird.
7. We will hide **here** in the cave.
8. The animal moved **again**.
9. The deer was **beautiful**.
10. The girl **thought** of all the animals she liked.

117

Hiding Places

by JULIE SMALL

Mom had to work in the country again.
She was going to photograph animals.
This time, she asked Sally to come.

"Mom, what can I do?" said Sally.

"You can help me," said Mom.
"Use your camera.
You can take photographs with me."

118

Then they came to a quiet, open place.
"This is the best place to find animals,"
said Mom.
"We can use the cameras here."

They sat on a hill next to a creek.

Mom sat on the grass.
She was looking for animals.

Sally was taking photographs
of the flowers next to the creek.
Sally thought she saw
a blue flower move.
She looked again.
But it turned out to be a blue bird.
Sally photographed it.
"The bird is blue like the flower,"
she thought.

Sally saw something in the grass jump.
Then she did not see it.
All she saw was a rock with a tail.
Then the rock jumped.
Sally looked again.

"That is not a rock," Sally thought.
"It is a rabbit that can look like a rock.
What a nice way to hide."

Sally photographed the rabbit.

"Come here, Sally," said Mom.
"Can you see the deer?"

"No.
Where is it?" Sally asked.

"It was drinking from the creek,"
said Mom.
"But now it is hiding next to the tree.
Look!
There it is!"

This time Sally saw the deer.
It was the color of the tree.
That is why Sally had not seen it.
Sally photographed the deer.

Sally watched for a long time.
Then she asked, "Mom, why did
that deer look like the tree?"

"Animals need to hide," said Mom.
"They need to hide from other animals
and people.
My job this time is to find out
how they can do that."

On the way home, Sally said,
"Peacocks are beautiful.
They have beautiful tails
with many colors.
How do they hide the tails?"

"Peacocks come from other lands,"
said Mom.
"The trees and grass in other places
are not like they are here.
There, peacocks hide in high grass."

One day, Mom came home from work
holding something.
"Look, Sally," she said.
"Open it and see what we did."

Sally opened it.
"My photographs!" she yelled.
"Look how well the deer can hide.
And look at the beautiful colors!"

"Your photographs and my photographs
worked well," said Mom.
"You can't hide that!"

125

A Rainbow for Me

adapted from a story by DON FREEMAN

One day I saw a rainbow
in the valley.
The rainbow was beautiful.
I wanted it to be my rainbow.

I put on my hat and ran out.
I ran fast as the wind.
But when I got to the valley,
the rainbow was not there.

126

I thought, one day when it rains,
a rainbow will come.
I will be in this valley
when it comes.
I will feel something moving like
the wings of a bird in back of me.
When I turn and look, my rainbow
will be following me!

My rainbow will want to play.
I will see that from the way it dances
up and down.

I will jump behind my rainbow.
My rainbow will jump next to me.
Then I will go up to the top
of my rainbow and run back down!

My rainbow will make a peacock tail
for me to see.
Then the rainbow will be a bed
where I can sleep.

Rainbows like to hide when they play.
My rainbow will hide from me.
Where do rainbows hide?
They hide in the flowers!
Flowers look a lot like a rainbow.
I can see my rainbow.
Can you?

But then the sun came out again.
My play thoughts disappeared.
And my play rainbow disappeared
the way rainbows do.
I turned and went back to my house.

I ran in the house.
There was a rainbow!
The sun and the water had made
a rainbow.
They had made a rainbow for me!

Dreams

LEARN NEW WORDS

1. I pushed the button and said, "**Click.**"
2. I made a kite for **him.**
3. The cat got a **hug** from David.
4. He smiled and **waved** to her.
5. I like to visit the pet **shop**.
6. Open the can of cat **food**.
7. We went **past** the big oak tree.
8. The flower pots are in the **windows**.
9. I **believe** what he said.
10. Where will the bus **stop**?

132

David's Windows

by ALICE LOW

Windows!
I like to look in and out
of windows.
This is what I like to do best.
There is something new to see
all the time.

One day, I was going to visit Grandma
in the country.
Mom was going to take me on the bus.

"David, I believe it is time to go,"
said Mom.
"Look for your hat."

"I <u>am</u> looking," I said.
But I was looking out the window.

"No time for windows now," said Mom.

I got my hat, and we went out.

134

"Look at that puppy!" I yelled
as we went past the pet shop.
"Look at him looking at me!"

"We do not have time to stop,"
said Mom.

"Look at the green kite," I said
as we went past the kite shop.

"We can't stop now," said Mom.

"Look at all that food," I said
as we went past the food shop.

"That looks nice," said Mom.
"But we have no time now."

135

We got two tickets and went on the bus.
It had long and high windows.

"I will use my make-believe camera,"
I thought.

I pushed the make-believe button on my
make-believe camera and said, "Click!"

I looked out the window at the houses
and shops—click!
I looked at the trees and the grass
in the country—click!

136

There was a lot of time to look at things.
Click, click, click!

Then the bus came to a stop.
I saw Grandma and waved.
She waved back at me and Mom.

"How nice to see you!" said Grandma.

I got a hug from Grandma.
Mom got a hug, too.
Then Mom got on the bus again
to go back home.

"I have to get two or three things
on the way home," said Grandma.
"I believe we have time to stop."

"More windows to look in!" I thought.

We went past the hat shop.
I looked at all the hats.
We went past the flower shop.
I got a flower for Grandma.
Then I got a card for Mom.
Grandma saw a friend
and waved to him.
I waved to him, too.
There is time to do a lot of things
in the country.

138

The sun was going down.
Grandma got oranges at the food shop,
and then we went home.
On the way, we looked at the windows
in all the houses.
Grandma likes to look, too.

In Grandma's house, my bed
is next to the window.
There is a tree under the window.
A bird house is in the tree.

"Can I look out the window one more time?" I asked Grandma.
"I want to see the bird."

"I believe it is time for bed now," said Grandma.
"When you get up, there will be many windows for you to look at!"

Grandma got a big hug from me.

"Sleep well, David," she said.

140

LEARN NEW WORDS

1. I was **dreaming** of funny things.
2. Come for a **ride** with me.
3. It is fun to **skate**.
4. That **horse** runs fast.
5. At **last**, I dreamed I saw a bird.
6. Look at the big, yellow **moon**!
7. The deer jumped **over** the creek.
8. No one **could** skate like him.
9. **First**, it rained, and then the sun came out.
10. He likes to ride on the **train**.

141

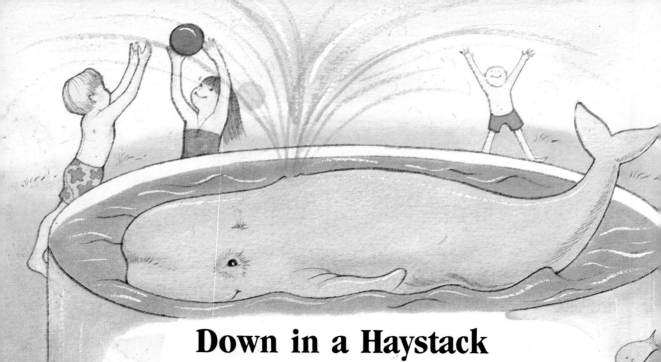

Down in a Haystack

adapted from a story by MICHAEL SAGE

Down in a haystack, Sandy
was sleeping.
He was dreaming, too.

First, Sandy dreamed he was a whale.
He made waves in the water.
He played with boys and girls.
It was fun being a whale!

Next, Sandy dreamed he was a bird.
He could fly high.
He could fly as high as the moon.

Sandy saw the wind take a boy's hat.
Sandy got the hat back for him.
The boy was happy to get his hat back.
Then Sandy helped get hats
for more people.

143

Sandy dreamed he was a kangaroo, too.
He wanted to jump over the moon.

First, he jumped over a fence.
Then, he jumped over a train.
Next, he jumped over a house.
Last, he jumped high up over the moon!

144

In one dream, Sandy was a big octopus.
As a big octopus, Sandy liked to skate.
He put skates on all his hands.
No one could skate as well as Sandy.

145

In his next dream, Sandy changed
to a horse.
He was a beautiful, fast horse.
Sandy could run as fast as a train.
No other horse could run
as fast as Sandy!

146

Sandy dreamed he was a hippopotamus.
Boys and girls wanted to ride
on his back.
First, they got rides to the train.
Then they got rides all over the fair.

Sandy had a big back!

147

At last, Sandy dreamed he was
a little puppy.
Then he got up out of the haystack.
"That is funny," Sandy said.
"I was a puppy in my last dream.
But I <u>am</u> a puppy!
I like being a puppy best of all."

148

LEARN NEW WORDS

1. Look at the **clock**, and tell me the time.
2. The boy has a red **coat**.
3. She **picked** up all the oak leaves.
4. He handed the **stick** to him.
5. It is **cold** out!
6. We will have a **great** time.
7. The food is in the **kitchen**.
8. He drinks a lot of **milk**.
9. I **counted** the sticks.
10. Put **everything** in this flat box.

149

One More Thing, Dad

adapted from a story by SUSAN L. THOMPSON

Dad was fixing a clock in the kitchen.

"I am going out, Dad," Caleb said.
"Can I take that orange with me?"

Dad handed Caleb the big orange.
Caleb turned the orange in his hands.
"That is 1," he said.

"Did you want something more?"
asked Dad.

150

"I had better take a sandwich, too,"
said Caleb.

"You can make one," said Dad.

Caleb made a great big sandwich.
"That is 2," he said.

Then Caleb saw the milk.
"Milk is nice with a sandwich," he said.

Caleb got the milk.
"That is 3," he counted.

151

"I could use a celery stick, too,"
said Caleb.

"Could you?" said Dad with a smile.
He handed Caleb a green celery stick.

"This celery stick is 4," said Caleb.
Caleb put all his food in a big sack.
He picked up the sack and counted
everything.
"1, 2, 3, 4," Caleb counted.

"Now I need one of my play people,"
he said.

Caleb came back to the kitchen
with one of his play people.
He put it next to the sack.
"That is 5," he said.

Then Caleb said, "It looks cold out.
Do you think I will need a blanket?"

Dad smiled as he worked on the clock.
"It is cold," he said.
"You can take your blue blanket."

Caleb ran to get the blanket.
"That is 6," he counted.

On the way back to the kitchen,
Caleb ran past his cat.

"Do you think the cat wants
to come with me?" Caleb asked.

"Why not?" said Dad.
"Take the cat with you."

Caleb picked up his cat and said,
"That is 7."

"Now I will put on my red coat.
My coat will be 8," said Caleb.
"Do you think I could use your scarf,
Dad?
Then I will not be cold."

"It is yours," Dad said.
He handed Caleb a folded scarf
as yellow as the sun.

"That is 9," said Caleb.
"I will not be cold with a coat
and a scarf."

155

"Now I have 9 things," said Caleb.
"1, 2, 3, 4, 5, 6, 7, 8, 9!"

"Do you have everything you need,
Caleb?" Dad asked.

"Everything!" Caleb said.
Dad helped Caleb
pick up all his things.
"Thanks, Dad."

"Have a great time!" said Dad.

Dad waved as Caleb went out.
Then he went back to work on the clock.

But Caleb came back to the kitchen.
"1, 2, 3, 4, 5, 6, 7, 8, 9,"
Caleb counted.

"What is it, Caleb?" Dad asked.
"I thought you had everything."

"There is <u>one</u> <u>more</u> thing, Dad,"
Caleb said.
"Will you come with me?"

"Why, thank you, Caleb," said Dad.
"I will come with you."

"Then you will make 10,"
Caleb smiled.
"You are a great big 10!
1, 2, 3, 4, 5, 6, 7, 8, 9, 10!"

LEARN NEW WORDS

1. She **held** on to her dreams.
2. The little boy was **sick**.
3. A **doctor** helps sick people.
4. The man was a **leader** of his people.
5. The **stars** are in beautiful costumes.
6. **Who** will be a great leader?
7. Many **women** work.
8. I like to **laugh** at the funny animals.
9. Do you want to fly in **space**?
10. **Write** your name on the paper.

159

Dreams at Work

by LINDA BEECH

A dream is like a kite.
Hold on to it, and follow it.

Louis Braille held a dream.
Louis wanted to read.
But he could not see.
That did not stop him.
He made a new alphabet he could feel.
Then he used his hands to read.
Louis's alphabet is named for him.
Now many people who can't see
can read.
They read in Braille.

160

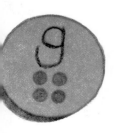

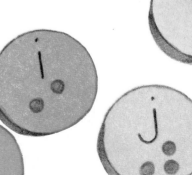

In the 1840s, Elizabeth Blackwell
wanted to be a doctor.
Elizabeth wanted to help sick people.
But at that time people said women
could not be doctors.
Elizabeth did not believe this.
She held on to her dream.
She worked and worked.

At last, she was a doctor.
Then she went where sick people
needed her.
Elizabeth was a leader for others
who held dreams as she did.

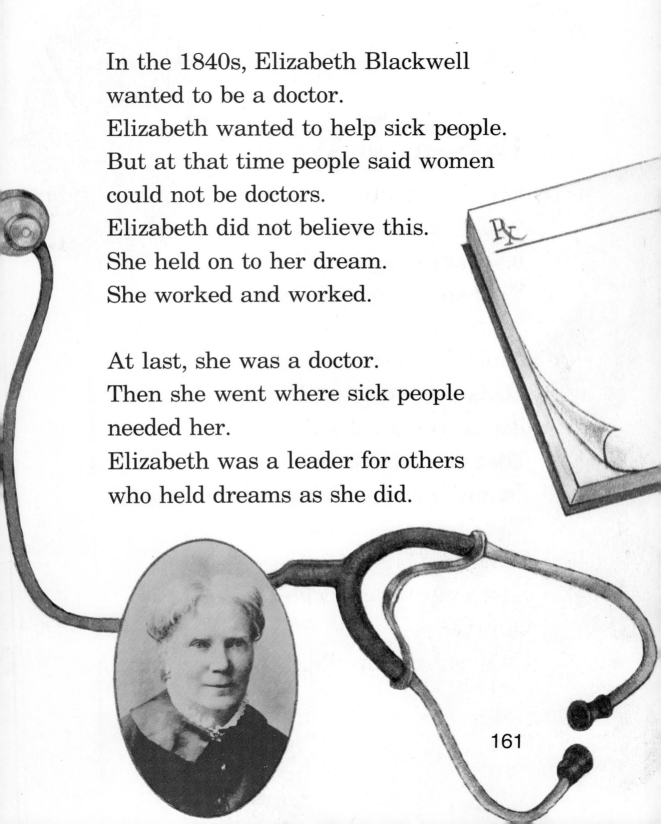

161

When Sequoyah was little, he was sick.
He could not play or work like others.
At home, he helped make things.

One day, he saw a man write.
It was the first time Sequoyah had seen
people write.
He had a thought.
"Could I make a Cherokee alphabet?"

Sequoyah did!
His alphabet was a great gift.
Now his people could write in Cherokee.
Sequoyah was a leader who helped
his people.

162

Walt Disney wanted people to laugh.
He made cartoons.
Then he thought of using animal stars
in his cartoons.
First, there was Mickey Mouse.
Then came Donald Duck and others.

Walt's cartoon stars made people laugh.
Then he opened places
for people to visit and have fun.
People came from all over the country.
They laughed and had a lot of fun.
They said Walt Disney was a great man
for helping make people happy.

Do you dream of going out in space?
Do you want to visit the moon?
Sally Ride had dreams of doing all of this.
And one day she did fly in space.

Sally is one of the astronauts.
Her job takes time and work.
She has to be fit.
She has to feel at home in space.
Not many astronauts are women.
Sally is one of the first women
to be one.
She is a leader for other people
who will one day visit the stars.

Fly Pretty Bird

by GLADYS WEEKS

Fly pretty bird
       fly,
as far
     as your wings
can take you.
I wish I could
       be
one of your wings
and fly
      along with you.

CASEY and the CLOCK

by CHRISTINE ECONOMOS

Mr. Tex was Casey's best friend.
She wanted to play with him.
But Mr. Tex could not play then.
He had a job to do.
"I have to fix this train," he said.

"Can I watch?" asked Casey.

"That will be nice," said Mr. Tex.

Casey watched him work.
Then she said, "What was it like
when the first trains came here?"

"See that clock?" said Mr. Tex.
"That clock was new when the first
trains came.
In a way, that clock saw all
that went on."

"Back then, people put big boxes of gold on this train," said Mr. Tex.
"But one day, a man named Clint came to take all the gold.
Clint got the gold and ran.
Many people followed him.
They got Clint.
But they never did find that gold!"

Mr. Tex looked back at the clock.
"I have to fix that train now.
I will be back, Casey," he said.

168

Casey looked at the clock.

The hands of the clock moved.

Click . . . click . . . click.

Casey went to sleep.

In her dreams, Casey was flying up to the clock.

Then she was on one of the clock's hands.

The hand turned and turned.

Casey was going back in time.

"Do you see what I see?" said the clock.
"That man is Clint.
He has come to take the gold.
Look how he puts it in that sack."

"I see him!" said Casey.
"Now I see people following him.
Look at Clint ride!
But he has no sack with him.
Where did he put the gold?"

170

"Clint hides in a cave,"
the clock said.
"The people find him in the cave.
But they do not find the gold.
They look, but they never
do find it.
They do not see what I see."

"What do you see?" asked Casey.

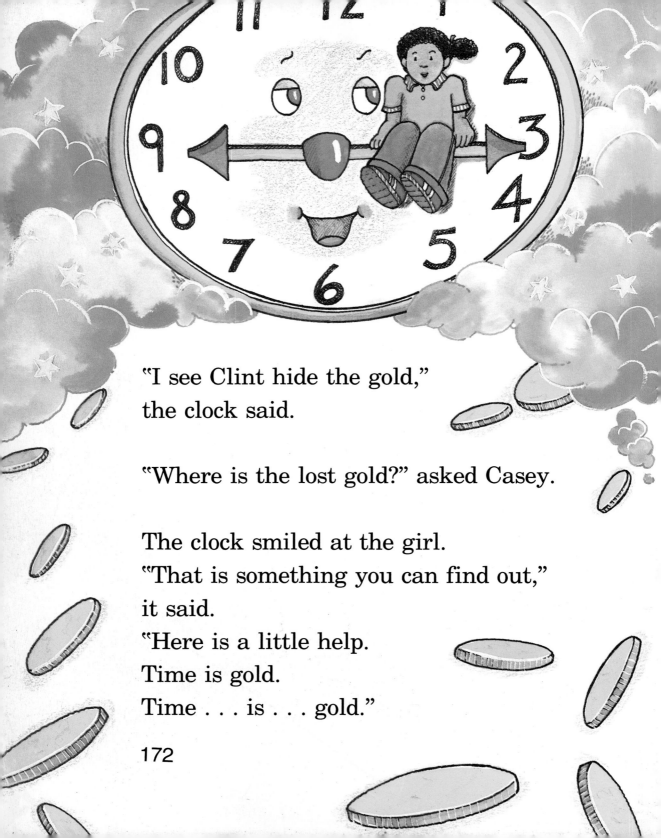

"I see Clint hide the gold,"
the clock said.

"Where is the lost gold?" asked Casey.

The clock smiled at the girl.
"That is something you can find out,"
it said.
"Here is a little help.
Time is gold.
Time . . . is . . . gold."

172

Casey got up.
"What a dream I had," Casey said.
"I have to tell Mr. Tex
that I can find the gold."

Mr. Tex followed Casey to the clock.
They looked in and saw a sack.
"It is the gold!" laughed Mr. Tex.
"Casey, how did you find it?"

Casey looked up at the clock.
She thought she saw the clock smile.

NEW WORDS

Following are the Instructional Words included in Level 5. The page number in parentheses refers to "Learn New Words," where the words in a lesson are introduced. The page number after each new word reflects the first time that word is used in a selection.

Lesson 1	**(8)**	**Lesson 3**	**(27)**	**Lesson 6**	**(50)**
back	13	dance	30	asked	51
band	10	fix	32	drink	57
box	11	plants	31	filled	52
come	14	puppy	31	flat	54
fair	9	song	30	mean	51
feel	10	things	28	move	52
happy	9	think	28	smiled	53
paint	13	well	30	thank	53
				your	51
Lesson 2	**(17)**	**Lesson 4**	**(34)**		
caves	24	fall	37	**Lesson 7**	**(60)**
change	19	hand	37	cleaned	65
fire	19	her	36	from	64
friends	18	hold	37	gift	61
gold	23	reads	36	his	63
hurt	19	she	36	house	62
lost	23	sisters	35	nest	64
nice	21	turns	36	paper	64